WORKBOOK

PEARSON EDEXCEL A-LEVEL

Politics 4

GLOBAL POLITICS

John Jefferies

HODDER
EDUCATION
AN HACHETTE UK COMPANY

Every effort has been made to trace all copyright holders, but if any have been inadvertently overlooked, the Publishers will be pleased to make the necessary arrangements at the first opportunity.

Although every effort has been made to ensure that website addresses are correct at time of going to press, Hodder Education cannot be held responsible for the content of any website mentioned in this book. It is sometimes possible to find a relocated web page by typing in the address of the home page for a website in the URL window of your browser.

Hachette UK's policy is to use papers that are natural, renewable and recyclable products and made from wood grown in well-managed forests and other controlled sources. The logging and manufacturing processes are expected to conform to the environmental regulations of the country of origin.

Orders: please contact Hachette UK Distribution, Hely Hutchinson Centre, Milton Road, Didcot, Oxfordshire, OX11 7HH. Telephone: +44 (0)1235 827827. Email education@hachette. co.uk. Lines are open from 9 a.m. to 5 p.m., Monday to Friday. You can also order through our website: www.hoddereducation.co.uk

ISBN: 978 1 3983 3248 5

© John Jefferies 2022

First published in 2022 by
Hodder Education,
An Hachette UK Company
Carmelite House
50 Victoria Embankment
London EC4Y 0DZ

www.hoddereducation.co.uk

Impression number   10 9 8 7 6 5 4 3 2 1

Year   2026 2025 2024 2023 2022

Cover photo © Chantal Cecchetti – stock.adobe.com

Typeset in India

Printed in India

A catalogue record for this title is available from the British Library.

Contents

About this book

1 This workbook will help you to prepare for the Global Politics (3B) exam.

2 This is the third exam which you will take and it is divided into three sections.

3 There are 84 marks available on this paper and it is worth a third of your A level marks.

4 The exam lasts two hours.

5 In Section A there will be two comparative questions, each worth 12 marks. You should attempt one of them. These questions always begin with the word 'Examine' and require you to investigate two areas which you will have studied in Global Politics. Six marks will be available for knowledge and understanding (AO1) and six marks will be available for analysis (AO2).

6 In Section B there is only one compulsory 12-mark question. This will always begin with the word 'Analyse' and requires you to focus on the way in which the international political theories of liberalism and realism can be used to interpret key developments in global politics. As with Section A, six marks will be available for knowledge and understanding (AO1) and six marks will be available for analysis (AO2). This is the only synoptic part of the exam and so you are required to refer to your understanding of core political theory (module 1) in your answer.

7 In Section C there will be three essays, each worth 30 marks. You must attempt two of them. 10 marks will be available for knowledge and understanding (AO1), 10 marks will be available for analysis (AO2) and 10 marks will be available for evaluation (AO3). The question will always begin with the word 'Evaluate' and the addition of AO3 marks means that you will be expected to reach a judgement.

8 Section A should take you 15 minutes; Section B should take you 15 minutes; Section C should take you 90 minutes (45 minutes per essay).

9 The worked answers in this workbook and the essay plans in the online answers all show where the response achieves marks for AO1 (knowledge and understanding), AO2 (analysis) and AO3 (evaluation).

10 Remember, only 30-mark Section C essay questions require AO3 (evaluation), so some responses will simply focus on AO1 (knowledge and understanding) and AO2 (analysis) marks.

11 In this workbook, icons next to the question will help you to identify:

   where questions draw on synoptic knowledge, i.e. content from more than one topic

   60 how long this question should take you

12 You still need to read your textbook and refer to your revision guides and lesson notes.

13 Marks are indicated for all questions so that you can gauge the level of detail required in your answers.

14 Timings are given for the exam-style questions to make your practice as realistic as possible.

15 Answers are available at: www.hoddereducation.co.uk/workbookanswers.

Topic 1 Comparative theories
Main ideas of realism

Realists emphasise the primacy of the nation state in an anarchic world where there is no higher authority to ensure order and stability. Conflict is therefore inevitable, so nation states must protect themselves with military power and alliances to survive. Critics say that this creates a security dilemma, since these actions encourage other nation states to respond in the same way, so making global relations more dangerous. Since realists believe that nation states pursue their own interests above everything else, they are sceptical about regional and global governance.

Practice questions ?

AO1 Knowledge and understanding

1 Define 'realism'. 2 marks

2 What do realists understand by the term 'global anarchy'? 2 marks

3 Why do realists believe that strife and conflict are inevitable in global politics? 2 marks

4 What do realists believe is the most effective way of securing global peace and stability? 2 marks

AO2 Analysis

5 How does conservative political theory relate to realism?   4 marks

Worked example

Conservative political theory underpins realism because traditional conservative thinkers such as Thomas Hobbes emphasise human beings' tendency to greed and violence. Consequently, nation states, like human beings, are predatory. Therefore, realism is concerned with maintaining the security and independence of the nation state in an anarchic world order in which there is no 'night watchman' (according to the realist thinker John Mearsheimer) to provide rules-based order. Both theories therefore prioritise survival in a dangerous world over more moral considerations.

> AO1 The answer refers to three conservative thinkers and a realist thinker. The clear connection made with core political theory meets the requirement for synopticity.

Conservatism also rejects principled attempts to perfect humanity. Edmund Burke was critical of the French Revolution because its aims were utopian, while according to Michael Oakeshott the aim of government is no more than 'to keep afloat on an even keel'. The ideas of both conservative thinkers underpin realism because realists are highly sceptical of idealistic attempts to construct institutions of regional or global governance which will encourage perpetual peace. According to the same principle, realists reject as dangerously destabilising humanitarian interventions that interfere with state sovereignty. Realism's emphasis on pragmatic considerations of national survival rather than anything more idealistic therefore firmly places it within the conservative tradition.

> AO2 Includes helpful analytical language such as 'underpin' and 'According to the same principle'.

6 Why do realists believe that the protection of human rights should not determine a nation state's foreign policy?   4 marks

Worked example

According to realism, the fundamental purpose of the nation state is survival in an anarchic world in which all states are power maximisers competing for power and influence. This means that the purpose of a nation state's foreign policy should be to enhance its security in a Hobbesian world of unending conflict. Therefore, the protection of human rights and launching humanitarian actions have no place in foreign policy because they distract the nation state from its primary purpose, which is to maintain its own survival.

> AO1 The answer uses appropriate terminology such as 'anarchic' and 'power maximisers'. The reference to NATO's intervention in Libya is appropriate and adds conviction. The connection made to Thomas Hobbes meets the requirement for synopticity.

National sovereignty is also fundamental to realism. As a result of this, the nation state alone determines the nature and extent of its citizens' civil liberties. Therefore, no outside force possesses the supranational authority to intervene within the borders of a sovereign nation state in order to impose its own standard of human rights. Since respect for national borders is the best guarantee of stability, such interventions can also be highly destabilising — e.g. NATO's intervention in Libya in 2011 was designed to reduce human suffering. However, realists claim that instead it destabilised the whole region, so increasing violence and leading to further human rights violations.

> AO2 Throughout the response the realist distrust of human rights protection is clearly explained, giving a highly focused and analytical response.

7   Why does realist political theory undermine the effectiveness of the United Nations?   4 marks

....

....

....

....

8   Why are realists more likely to support military alliances such as NATO than they are to favour regional organisations such as the European Union?   4 marks

....

....

....

....

Main ideas of liberalism

Liberals possess an optimistic approach to global politics based on human beings' capacity for rational and moral actions. They believe that in addition to the nation state there are many other important decision-makers in global politics and that they can work together to achieve harmony and balance. When this occurs, a web of complex independence is created in which mutually beneficial outcomes can be achieved. Liberals are therefore much more supportive of regional and global governance.

Practice questions ?

AO1 Knowledge and understanding

9   Define 'liberalism'.   2 marks

....

....

10 How does liberalism connect to free trade?   2 marks

....

....

11 What is the connection between liberalism and regionalism?   2 marks

....

....

12 Why do liberals believe that democracy is the best form of government?   2 marks

....

....

13 How does core political theory underpin a liberal approach to global politics?   4 marks

....

....

....

....

14 Why do liberals believe that the protection of human rights should play an important role in global politics?   4 marks

....

....

....

....

15 Why do liberals argue that collective dilemmas such as climate change cannot be resolved by a realist approach to global politics?   4 marks

....

....

....

....

16 Why do liberals believe that democracies are less likely to go to war than semi-autocratic and autocratic states?   4 marks

....

....

....

....

Divisions between realism and liberalism

Realists and liberals possess fundamentally different attitudes towards human nature, security, the role of the nation state and the likelihood of conflict. Since liberals believe human beings can act rationally and morally, they encourage cooperation in regional and international organs of governance. However, realists believe that the anarchic nature of global relations and the predatory impulse of human beings mean that the nation state's primary goal must be to maintain its sovereign existence. They therefore differ over the extent to which respect for human rights should influence foreign policy and whether the nation state should accept limits on its sovereignty.

AO1 Knowledge and understanding

17 Why are the views of realists and liberals so different regarding the importance of sovereignty in global relations? 2 marks

....

....

18 In what ways do realists and liberals differ over humanitarian intervention? 2 marks

....

....

19 How do realists and liberals differ over the desirability of regional and global governance? 2 marks

....

....

20 Why do realists and liberals disagree over whether conflict is inevitable in global relations? 2 marks

....

....

AO2 Analysis

21 Why do liberals and realists differ so much in their approach to the balance of power? 4 marks

....

....

....

22 How are the attitudes of liberals and realists towards democracy different? 4 marks

....

....

....

23 In what ways does the concept of a universal standard of human rights divide liberals and realists? 4 marks

....

....

....

24 Why do liberals and realists differ in their attitude towards the desirability of world government?

4 marks

....

....

....

Main ideas of the anarchical society and society of states theory

Anarchical society (society of states) theory was developed by the political theorist Hedley Bull. It is based on the principle that, since global politics is anarchic, there is no supranational authority which can compel the obedience of nation states. It also acknowledges the realist principle that nation states act out of self-interest. However, it recognises that nation states can make the rational decision to work with other nation states in order to achieve mutually beneficial outcomes. Therefore, it is possible to construct a relatively stable society of states based upon realist self-interest rather than liberal idealism.

Practice questions ?

AO1 Knowledge and understanding

25 In what ways is anarchical society/society of states theory different from a liberal interpretation of global politics?

2 marks

....

....

26 In what ways is anarchical society/society of states theory different from a realist interpretation of global politics?

2 marks

....

....

AO2 Analysis

27 In what circumstances can it be said that global politics conforms to anarchical society/society of states theory?

4 marks

....

....

....

28 Why could it be argued that contemporary global politics does not conform to anarchical society/society of states theory?

4 marks

....

....

....

An evaluation of the extent to which realism and liberalism explain recent developments in global politics

In order to assess the extent to which liberalism or realism has guided global politics since 2000, you should investigate the relationship between the state and globalisation. In this context, you should address the extent to which global governance (political, economic, human rights and environmental) has developed according to liberal or realist principles. The way in which nation states, the European Union (EU) and other regional bodies approach current developments in global relations should also be contextualised within a realist/liberal framework.

Practice questions ?

AO1 Knowledge and understanding

29 In what ways was the establishment of the International Criminal Court in 2002 an example of liberalism? **2 marks**

....

....

30 Why is UN Responsibility to Protect (2005) an example of liberalism? **2 marks**

....

....

31 How have Russia and China followed a realist foreign policy in recent years? **2 marks**

....

....

32 What is the connection between liberalism and the expansion of the EU in 2004, 2007 and 2013? **2 marks**

....

....

AO2 Analysis

33 Why has the Syrian conflict (2011–) so bitterly divided realists and liberals? **4 marks**

....

....

....

....

....

....

34 Why are liberals often so concerned about the rise of China?

4 marks

....

....

....

....

35 Has the way in which nation states have responded to climate change since 2015 conformed more to a realist or a liberal interpretation of global politics?

4 marks

....

....

....

....

36 To what extent are liberals more likely to favour the policies of the Biden administration (2021–) over the Trump administration (2017–21)?

4 marks

....

....

....

....

Exam-style questions ?

Paper 3 Section B

1 Analyse the reasons why realists and liberals view alliance building and increased military spending by nation states so differently. In your answer you must discuss any relevant core political ideas. **12 marks**

Write a bullet point plan here, then use a separate sheet of paper to answer the question in full. 15

....

....

....

....

2 Analyse the differences which exist between realists and liberals over the role of the nation state in global politics. **12 marks**

Write a bullet point plan here, then use a separate sheet of paper to answer the question in full. 15

....

....

....

....

Topic 2 The state and globalisation

The nation state and national sovereignty

The nation state is a political community constructed on shared citizenship and nationality. According to realists the nation state is sovereign and so should possess absolute authority over everything that occurs within its borders. These principles derive from the Peace of Westphalia (1648), which emphasised the inviolability of national sovereignty. According to realists there is no authority greater than that of the nation state.

Practice questions ?

AO1 Knowledge and understanding

1 What are Westphalian principles of state sovereignty?   2 marks

....

....

2 What do you understand by the concept of the nation state?   2 marks

....

....

3 How are realists sceptical of regional governance?   2 marks

....

....

4 What is the meaning and significance of the billiard ball model of global relations?   2 marks

....

....

AO2 and AO3 Analysis and evaluation

5 In what ways can a Westphalian approach to international relations be criticised?   4 marks

Worked example

Liberals reject a Westphalian approach to international relations because they argue that its commitment to national sovereignty does not provide an effective way of resolving global collective dilemmas such as climate change and the Covid-19 pandemic. The success, for example, of climate change agreements such as Paris (2015) has been undermined by nation states not accepting externally imposed mandatory cuts in their carbon emissions. Additionally, if nation states prioritise their national security and fail to cooperate with other nation states, then global relations will always be defined by fear, suspicion and resentment. This is likely to provoke a 'security dilemma' as the build-up of arms by nation states to protect themselves leads to others doing the same, so increasing tension. A commitment

> AO1 The response is firmly based in well-understood evidence. The early reference to liberalism provides appropriate context.

to national sovereignty also reduces the effectiveness of liberal organs of global governance such as the United Nations, making it more difficult to resolve collective dilemmas such as international terrorism and failed states. A Westphalian approach to global politics also makes it impossible to achieve a universally applicable international standard of human rights. Therefore, attempts to enhance human rights protection through the International Criminal Court and UN Responsibility to Protect will fail. In short, critics argue that the challenges facing the world cannot be resolved unless nation states abandon a Westphalian approach to global politics by accepting some limits on their sovereign independence.

> **AO2** No evaluative (AO3) judgement is required, so the answer correctly focuses on explaining why the Westphalian approach can be criticised.

6 To what extent has globalisation reduced the importance of the nation state in global politics?

4 marks

Worked example

Following the end of the Cold War in 1991 it was widely assumed by liberal theorists that the nation state would become less important in global politics. This was because the economic pressure to conform to the free market principles of the Washington Consensus (economic neo-liberalism) would reduce nation states' ability to determine economic policy. Political globalisation would also create new opportunities for nation states to work together and with non-state actors through regional and global institutions of governance. UN Responsibility to Protect (2005) even suggested that the international community could intervene within a nation state if it was abusing the human rights of its citizens. Cultural globalisation would further reduce the centrality of the nation state in people's lives by creating a global marketplace of choice, providing new non-state loyalties and enthusiasms.

> **AO1** The evidence supplied is thorough and appropriate.

> **AO2** The way in which different types of globalisation impact on national sovereignty is clearly explained with a focus on answering the question.

However, the impact of globalisation on the nation state has been much more complicated. Although there is considerable pressure through the WTO, IMF and World Bank to conform to the global free market, most nation states still control their fiscal and monetary policy and powerful countries like the USA can engage in protectionism as an economic weapon. There has also been a reaction against the Americanisation of global culture, leading to an unexpected rise in populist nationalism in Russia, Hungary, Turkey and China. The internet can further encourage this by providing the means by which nation states can expand their nationalist agenda globally (RT/Russia Today). The way in which economic globalisation has increased the wealth of emerging nation states like China and India has also reinforced their sense of national identity. This has made them assert their national interests more in global politics, as can be seen with China's military expansion in the South China Sea. This, therefore, suggests that rather than diminishing the role of the nation state in international relations, globalisation may actually have increased it.

> **AO3** Evaluation is very strong. The implications of the evidence are thoroughly explored, leading to a controversial, interesting and strongly supported judgement.

7   Why are realists so sceptical of liberal attempts to establish regional and global
    institutions of human rights protection? 4 marks

....

....

....

....

8   To what extent do Westphalian principles of state sovereignty undermine attempts
    to establish an international standard of human-rights protection? 4 marks

....

....

....

....

Globalisation

As a result of diverse forms of globalisation (economic, political and cultural), the
world has become more widely and deeply connected, making nation states more
interdependent. The sovereignty of the nation state has also been challenged in
areas such as the state's control over its citizens and the potential for humanitarian
intervention. Hyper-globalisers argue that globalisation has dramatically reduced
the role of the nation state in global politics. Globalisation sceptics dispute this
and transformationalists argue that the nation state has adapted itself to new
global realities. Liberals are optimistic that globalisation can encourage greater
global cooperation. Realists respond that nation states remain dominant and utilise
globalisation to their own advantage.

Practice questions ?

AO1 Knowledge and understanding

9   How does the World Bank encourage economic growth in the developing world? 2 marks

....

....

10 What is cultural globalisation and how has it contributed to a homogenisation of
    global culture? 2 marks

....

....

11 How do hyper-globalisers view globalisation? 2 marks

....

....

12 How do globalisation sceptics view globalisation?

2 marks

....

....

13 What is the cobweb model of global relations and how does it provide a liberal alternative to a realist approach to international relations?

4 marks

....

....

....

....

14 Why do liberals and realists differ so strongly over the desirability of humanitarian interventions?

4 marks

....

....

....

15 Why do classical liberals support economic globalisation?

4 marks

....

....

....

16 How significant has the impact of economic globalisation been?

4 marks

....

....

....

Debates about the impact of globalisation including its advantages and disadvantages

Globalisation challenges the independence and autonomy of the nation state. Supporters of globalisation claim that by widening and deepening global connectedness it provides new opportunities to establish a global community and resolve collective dilemmas. Critics claim that globalisation creates new problems that challenge global stability.

AO1 Knowledge and understanding

17 In what ways has economic globalisation challenged the North/South divide?　　2 marks

....

....

18 How does the European Union's Court of Justice challenge the sovereignty of
EU member states?　　2 marks

....

....

19 Explain how political globalisation opens up political decision making to
non-state actors.　　2 marks

....

....

20 Why has economic globalisation been criticised?　　2 marks

....

....

AO2 and AO3 Analysis and evaluation

21 Why is the United Nations' Responsibility to Protect (2005) so controversial?　　4 marks

....

....

....

....

22 To what extent does the European Court of Human Rights challenge the
sovereignty of its member states?　　4 marks

....

....

....

....

23 Explain the connection between the Covid-19 pandemic and globalisation.　　4 marks

....

....

....

....

24 Why is cultural globalisation increasingly being seen as more than just Americanisation?

4 marks

....

....

....

The ways in and extent to which globalisation addresses and resolves contemporary issues

The extent to which globalisation has been successful in protecting human rights, lessening poverty and resolving collective dilemmas such as climate change is controversial. Liberals view globalisation as essential in the establishment of a communal response to shared problems. Realists respond that globalisation has not challenged the nation state as the key decision-maker in global politics. Some issues such as climate change may be more difficult to resolve because of globalisation.

Practice questions ?

AO1 Knowledge and understanding

25 In what ways has economic globalisation helped to lessen poverty?

2 marks

....

....

26 How has globalisation encouraged environmental degradation?

2 marks

....

....

27 How does political globalisation enable nation states to resolve collective dilemmas?

2 marks

....

....

28 Why is globalisation often seen as advancing the interests of Western powers?

2 marks

....

....

AO2 and AO3 Analysis and evaluation

29 How significant has the impact of economic globalisation been on the global balance of power?

4 marks

....

....

....

30 Do all forms of globalisation impact equally on nation states? 4 marks

....

....

....

31 Why is the impact of cultural globalisation so controversial? 4 marks

....

....

....

32 Does political globalisation provide an effective response to the challenge of climate change? 4 marks

....

....

....

Exam-style questions **?**

Paper 3 Section A

1 Examine the main criticisms of economic globalisation and cultural globalisation. 12 marks

Write a plan here, then use a separate sheet of paper to answer the question in full. **15**

....

....

....

....

....

....

....

....

....

....

....

....

2 Examine the impact of globalisation on the USA and China.   12 marks

15

Write a plan here, then use a separate sheet of paper to answer the question in full.

....

....

....

....

....

....

....

....

....

Paper 3 Section C

3 Evaluate the extent to which globalisation has encouraged global interdependence and interconnectivity.   30 marks

45

Write a plan here, then use a separate sheet of paper to answer the question in full.

....

....

....

....

....

....

4 Evaluate the extent to which the main impact of globalisation has been to advance Western interests.   30 marks

45

Write a plan here, then use a separate sheet of paper to answer the question in full.

....

....

....

....

....

....

5   Evaluate the extent to which economic globalisation has had a more positive impact on the developing world than cultural globalisation.   **30 marks**

Write a plan here, then use a separate sheet of paper to answer the question in full.

....

....

....

....

....

....

....

6   Evaluate the extent to which the influence of the nation state in global politics has been significantly undermined by globalisation.   **30 marks**

Write a plan here, then use a separate sheet of paper to answer the question in full.

....

....

....

....

....

....

....

....

7   Evaluate the extent to which globalisation has made it difficult to resolve the challenge of climate change.   **30 marks**

Write a plan here, then use a separate sheet of paper to answer the question in full.

....

....

....

....

....

....

....

Topic 3 Global governance: political

The United Nations

The United Nations (UN) was established at the end of the Second World War (1945) in order to encourage global development, safeguard human rights and reduce the risk of further conflict. The extent to which the UN has succeeded in these objectives is controversial. For example, the significance and effectiveness of the Security Council, the General Assembly, the Economic and Social Council and the International Court of Justice (World Court) have all been questioned.

Practice questions ?

AO1 Knowledge and understanding

1 Explain how the UN Security Council is composed and what its powers are.　　2 marks

....

....

2 In what ways has the UN Security Council been criticised?　　2 marks

....

....

3 What is the purpose of the UN General Assembly?　　2 marks

....

....

4 What is the purpose of the UN Economic and Social Council?　　2 marks

....

....

AO2 and AO3 Analysis and evaluation

5 How justified are criticisms of UN peace-keeping operations?　　4 marks

Worked example

UN peace-keeping operations have often been criticised for lacking a sufficient mandate to protect human rights. In the 1990s, for example, UN peace-keepers in Bosnia were not supposed to engage in offensive military action. As a result, 7,000 men and boys were murdered when the safe-haven of Srebrenica was captured by Bosnian Serbs. Too often the UN has failed to learn from this lesson. UN blue helmets operating in South Sudan and the Democratic Republic of Congo have been criticised for having an insufficient military mandate to protect civilians and stop human rights abuses. This problem is compounded by the fact that UN member states only contribute $6.6 billion (2021) to pay for peace-keeping missions. Therefore, they are extremely under-resourced compared with

> **AO1** The evidence on UN peace-keeping operations is thorough and appropriate.

> **AO2** The implications of the evidence are clearly explained with a constant focus on answering the question.

the $733 billion US defence budget (2021). However, UN peace-keeping operations take place in some of the most lawless parts of the world, such as Mali and the Central African Republic. Before we are too critical, we should therefore acknowledge the massive problems they face, especially as they are often the only legitimate external military force in the region. When there is a viable political settlement to enforce and they are provided with robust rules of engagement, UN peace-keepers can also prove indispensable in establishing a transition to democracy, such as has occurred in Kosovo, Liberia and Côte d'Ivoire.

> **A03** Evaluation is very strong. The implications of the evidence are thoroughly explored, leading to a balanced judgement. A particular strength of the response is that evaluation occurs throughout, not simply at the end.

6 How convincing is the case for the reform of the UN Security Council? 	**4 marks**

Worked example

There is a strong case to reform the UN Security Council. The veto power of the Permanent Five means that the Security Council often lacks the necessary unanimity to take military action in crises such as the Syrian civil war. Critics further point out that the members of the Permanent Five represent the global balance of power in 1945 and so question the legitimacy of countries such as France and the UK still playing such a vital role in global decision making when their international influence has diminished. However, although these criticisms are valid, it is difficult to agree how best to reform the Security Council. If France and the UK were to lose their veto-wielding influence, there would be a strong case for Russia to lose its veto too, since its economy is significantly smaller. This, though, would be controversial given Russia's nuclear capability. On the other hand, if the Security Council expanded to include more veto-wielding members, it would create huge friction between states seeking the prestige of membership. Pakistan, for example, would be unlikely to accept India being a member of the Permanent Five. More permanent members, each with the veto, would also make it even more difficult to reach consensus. However, if the permanent members lost the veto, it could also undermine the legitimacy of UN military action, since the decision to deploy military force might not have unanimous support. This suggests that, although the case for reform of the UN Security Council might seem overwhelming, it could raise even more complicated problems.

> **A01** There is a clear understanding of the problems associated with the Security Council.

> **A02** A number of ways in which the Security Council could be reformed are outlined.

> **A03** The candidate strongly evaluates why these reforms would be problematic.

7 How powerful is the UN secretary–general? 	**4 marks**

....

....

....

....

8 Is the General Assembly a useful body?   4 marks

....

....

....

....

The North Atlantic Treaty Organization

In 1949, the North Atlantic Treaty Organization (NATO) was set up to protect western Europe from potential Soviet aggression. It is based on the principle of collective security (Article 5). Following the end of the Cold War it expanded its membership and engaged in several peace-making and peace-keeping operations. Some suggest it should now refocus on its original purpose of deterring potential Russian expansionism.

Practice questions ?

AO1 Knowledge and understanding

9 Why was NATO established in 1949?   2 marks

....

....

10 What is the significance of Article 5 (on collective security) of NATO's charter?   2 marks

....

....

11 What does acting 'out of area' mean? Provide two examples of when NATO has done this.   2 marks

....

....

12 How many new member states have joined NATO since the end of the Cold War? What has been their purpose in joining NATO?   2 marks

....

....

AO2 and AO3 Analysis and evaluation

13 Why have NATO's 'out of area' operations been criticised?   4 marks

....

....

....

14 In what ways might the membership of Hungary and Turkey be seen to weaken NATO?

4 marks

....

....

....

15 Why has NATO's expansion into eastern Europe been controversial?

4 marks

....

....

....

16 What are the main challenges to NATO's effectiveness?

4 marks

....

....

....

....

How effectively have the UN and NATO responded to contemporary global issues?

Although the UN is confronting pressing collective dilemmas such as climate change, its effectiveness is weakened by its lack of supranational authority. UN peace-keeping missions have also been criticised for being under-funded and ineffective. NATO is proving less prepared to engage in human rights enforcement operations as it reverts to its original purpose of protecting its members.

Practice questions ?

AO1 Knowledge and understanding

17 In what ways has the UN responded to the challenge of climate change?

2 marks

....

....

18 Outline two NATO interventions which were launched to protect human rights.

2 marks

....

....

19 Describe the work of two UN Economic and Social Council agencies in combating poverty/encouraging development.

2 marks

....

....

....

20 Explain the work of the UN Human Rights Council and the UN High Commissioner for Human Rights.

2 marks

....

....

....

AO2 and AO3 Analysis and evaluation

21 How effective is the UN's International Court of Justice (ICJ)?

4 marks

....

....

....

....

22 What factors undermine UN peace-keeping operations?

4 marks

....

....

....

....

23 Why have there been fewer humanitarian missions by NATO in recent years?

4 marks

....

....

....

....

24 How effective has the UN been in responding to the challenge of climate change?

4 marks

....

....

....

....

Paper 3 Section A

1 Examine the main obstacles which the United Nations faces in addressing issues connected with environmental protection and human rights enforcement.

12 marks

15

Write a plan here, then use a separate sheet of paper to answer the question in full.

....

....

....

....

....

....

....

....

....

....

2 Examine the ways in which NATO's approach to peace-keeping has remained the same and changed in the years since the end of the Cold War.

12 marks

15

Write a plan here, then use a separate sheet of paper to answer the question in full.

....

....

....

....

....

....

....

....

....

....

Paper 3 Section C

For questions 3–7, write a bullet point plan in the space provided, then use a separate sheet of paper to answer the questions in full.

3 Evaluate the extent to which the United Nations contributes more to conflict resolution than NATO does.

30 marks

45

....

....

....

....

4 Evaluate the view that the United Nations has failed to provide effective leadership when confronting the most serious challenges that the world faces.

30 marks

45

....

....

....

....

5 Evaluate the view that the United Nations has proved better in dealing with the challenge of climate change than in protecting human rights.

30 marks

45

....

....

....

....

6 Evaluate the view that NATO no longer provides its members with effective military protection.

30 marks

45

....

....

....

....

7 Evaluate the view that the United Nations is becoming less relevant in global relations.

30 marks

45

....

....

....

....

Topic 4 Global governance: economic

The International Monetary Fund and the World Bank

According to neo-classical development theory, trade liberalisation (free markets and free trade) provides the most effective way of encouraging global prosperity. This is facilitated by the World Bank and the International Monetary Fund (IMF), which encourage nation states to adapt to the global free market through structural adjustment programmes (SAPs). Critics claim that SAPs challenge sovereignty and are often inappropriate. World systems theory associates trade liberalisation with neo-colonialism and so is also highly critical of these institutions.

Practice questions ?

AO1 Knowledge and understanding

1 Explain how the IMF seeks to achieve global financial stability.   2 marks

....

....

2 What is the main purpose of the World Bank?   2 marks

....

....

3 How does the work of the IMF and the World Bank connect to neo-classical economic theory?   2 marks

....

....

4 Explain the world systems/dependency theory.   2 marks

....

....

AO2 and AO3 Analysis and evaluation

5 How valid are criticisms of World Bank structural adjustment programmes?   4 marks

Worked example

The World Bank requires nation states to introduce free market structural adjustment programmes in return for loans. This 'conditionality' has been criticised because structural adjustment programmes usually demand that the recipient country introduce radical reforms such as lowering tariffs and introducing privatisation and cuts in public spending. These reforms can lead to an increase in unemployment as industries are opened up to global competition. However, such reforms are often necessary if developing countries are to take

> **AO1** A clear explanation of what structural adjustment programmes are designed to do.

> **AO2** The criticisms of structural adjustment programmes are thoroughly explored.

advantage of growth sectors in which they have a comparative advantage in global trade. For example, World Bank structural adjustment programmes in Ghana devastated its rice economy by opening it up to foreign competition. However, this encouraged Ghana to move towards gold and cocoa manufacture, in which it has a natural advantage in global trade. Cuts in public spending are also controversial and often impact most on the poorest in society, who rely on government support. However, if public spending is too great, this can encourage inflation and make exports too expensive, stopping a developing state from taking advantage of new opportunities in global free trade.

> **A03** These criticisms are then evaluated, enabling a thoughtful assessment of a question which is often approached in a one-sided fashion.

6 How convincing is the criticism that the IMF and the World Bank encourage neo-colonial dependency?

4 marks

Worked example

Supporters of dependency/world systems theory claim that the IMF and the World Bank structural adjustment programmes encourage neo-colonial dependency. This is because by encouraging nation states in the developing world to open up their markets, they allow multinational corporations (MNCs) to sell cheap manufactured products to them. As a result, developing countries become dependent upon inexpensive manufactured goods being 'dumped' on them, so they never achieve industrialisation themselves. According to this theory, developing countries are kept in a peripheral economic status since they are made so dependent on core states for the manufactured goods they consume. This argument may be true of some of the least well-resourced countries in the world, which the economist Paul Collier refers to as 'The Bottom Billion'. However, most developing countries have some comparative advantage (David Ricardo) which they can exploit in a global free market. Therefore, World Bank/IMF free market reforms are more likely to enable them to utilise their skills and resources globally than condemn them to a neo-colonial status. For example, World Bank free market reforms in India in the 1990s encouraged India to move away from subsistence agriculture by utilising its massive labour force in manufacturing, telecommunications and data analysis. This has enabled India to have the sixth biggest GDP in the world in 2021.

> **A01** Clear detail suggesting strong understanding, shown also by the final sentence.

> **A02** The arguments for dependency/world systems theory are explained.

> **A03** A reasoned and forthright judgement is made by assessing the strength of these arguments.

7 Why has the IMF's response to the global economic problems created by the Covid-19 pandemic involved a radical departure from orthodox policy?

4 marks

....

....

....

....

8 How effectively has the World Bank responded to recent criticisms? 4 marks

....

....

....

....

The World Trade Organization and the G7 and G20

The World Trade Organization (WTO) encourages free trade between its 164 member states (2021). Critics claim that it favours the developed world over the developing world and that it should be more concerned with workers' rights and environmental protection.

The Group of Seven (G7) organises regular meetings between the nation states with the biggest economies in the developed world (the Global North). The Group of Twenty (G20) does the same for the world's biggest economies in the developed world (the Global North) *and* the developing world (the Global South). However, neither organisation can compel its members to act in a certain way and so the relevance of both organisations is hotly disputed.

Practice questions ?

AO1 Knowledge and understanding

9 What are the main aims of the WTO? 2 marks

....

....

10 What is the purpose of the G7? 2 marks

....

....

11 Explain the main differences between the membership of the G7 and the G20. 2 marks

....

....

....

12 In what ways have the G7 and the G20 been criticised? 2 marks

....

....

....

....

13 What criticisms have been levelled at the WTO by environmental and human rights groups?

4 marks

....

....

....

....

14 Why is the G7 controversial?

4 marks

....

....

....

....

15 Why has it been so difficult to achieve consensus on WTO trade rounds?

4 marks

....

....

....

....

16 How convincing is the claim that neo-classical economic theory promotes prosperity?

4 marks

....

....

....

....

Global economic governance and the issue of poverty

The North/South divide recognises the way in which economic power is divided between the developing world (the Global South) and the developed world (the Global North). Since the developing world is growing so fast economically, the usefulness of this term has become controversial. According to classical development theory, the growing convergence between the Global North and the Global South is due to the benefits of free trade. However, according to world systems theory, free trade encourages neo-colonial dependency. There is also considerable debate over whether poverty should only be measured in economic terms.

AO1 Knowledge and understanding

17 Explain the meaning of the term 'North/South divide' in global politics. 2 marks

....

....

18 Why do some critics suggest that the term 'North/South divide' is now obsolete? 2 marks

....

....

19 In what ways could it be argued that the Global South has benefited from the
implementation of neo-classical economic policies? 2 marks

....

....

20 What is the difference between the orthodox and alternative measurements
of poverty? 2 marks

....

....

AO2 and AO3 Analysis and evaluation

21 Why is the issue of protectionism/tariffs so controversial? 4 marks

....

....

....

....

22 Do you think that the term 'North/South divide' is still helpful? 4 marks

....

....

....

....

23 How convincing is the view that the orthodox measurement of poverty is an
unhelpful measurement? 4 marks

....

....

....

....

24 To what extent are neo-classical economic policies responsible for the North/South divide?

4 marks

....

....

....

....

Non-governmental organisations, poverty and development

Global civil society and non-state actors including non-governmental organisations (NGOs) play a leading role in development and poverty reduction. These include international charities such as Save the Children, faith-based organisations and global foundations such as the Bill & Melinda Gates Foundation. However, some critics question the effectiveness of overseas aid and even suggest that its contribution to development may be counterproductive.

AO1 Knowledge and understanding

25 Explain the meaning of the term 'overseas aid'.

2 marks

....

....

26 Explain two reasons why nation states may decide to provide overseas aid.

2 marks

....

....

27 Describe the work of two NGOs which provide overseas aid.

2 marks

....

....

....

....

28 Explain why overseas aid has been criticised.

2 marks

....

....

....

....

AO2 and AO3 Analysis and evaluation

29 In what ways has the structure of the World Bank and the IMF been criticised?   4 marks

....

....

....

....

....

....

30 What is the connection between economic globalisation and neo-colonialism?   4 marks

....

....

....

....

....

....

....

31 How convincing is the argument that even well-intentioned aid delivered by NGOs is unhelpful to the developing world?   4 marks

....

....

....

....

....

32 Do you agree that neo-classical economic policies have done more for the developing world than overseas aid?   4 marks

....

....

....

....

....

Paper 3 Section A

1 Examine the main differences between the Global North and the Global South. **12 marks** (15)

Write a plan here, then use a separate sheet of paper to answer the question in full.

....

....

....

....

....

....

....

....

....

....

2 Examine the main points of tension between neo-classical economic theory and dependency (world systems) theory. **12 marks** (15)

Write a plan here, then use a separate sheet of paper to answer the question in full.

....

....

....

....

....

....

....

....

....

....

....

....

Paper 3 Section C

For questions 3–7, write a bullet point plan in the space provided, then use a separate sheet of paper to answer the questions in full.

3   Evaluate the extent to which economic globalisation has made the concept of a North/South divide meaningless.   **30 marks**

....

....

....

....

4   Evaluate the extent to which neither the G7 nor the G20 plays a significant role in global economic governance.   **30 marks**

....

....

....

....

5   Evaluate the view that the International Monetary Fund and the World Bank have failed the world's poor.   **30 marks**

....

....

....

....

6   Evaluate the view that the World Trade Organization has done little to improve the lives of poor people in the developing world.   **30 marks**

....

....

....

....

7   Evaluate the view that non-governmental organisations contribute significantly more to poverty reduction in the developing world than the International Monetary Fund and the World Bank.   **30 marks**

....

....

....

....

Topic 5 Global governance: human rights

Origins and development of international law and institutions

As a result of massive human rights violations during the Second World War, the United Nations Declaration of Human Rights (1948) established a set of rights which all human beings possess. In this context several international courts and tribunals have been established to encourage respect for human rights-based international law. These include the International Court of Justice (ICJ), the European Court of Human Rights (ECHR), four UN tribunals (Yugoslavia, Rwanda, Sierra Leone and Cambodia) and the International Criminal Court (ICC).

Practice questions ?

AO1 Knowledge and understanding

1   What is the significance of the United Nations Universal Declaration of Human Rights?   2 marks

....

....

2   Why and with what purpose was the International Court of Justice established?   2 marks

....

....

3   How does the European Convention on Human Rights connect to the European Court of Human Rights?   2 marks

....

....

4   Why and with what purpose was the International Criminal Court established?   2 marks

....

....

AO2 and AO3 Analysis and evaluation

5   What is a universalist approach to human rights and why is it controversial?   4 marks

Worked example

The United Nations Universal Declaration of Human Rights was published in 1948. It represents a universalist approach to human rights and clearly states the human rights which all people can claim by virtue of their humanity. These rights are non-negotiable and include rights such as equality before the law, freedom of expression and the right to choose one's religion. According to supporters of the Universal Declaration of Human Rights, human rights transcend religious, cultural and social differences and so all human beings are eligible for the same rights. According to Eleanor Roosevelt, who chaired the committee which agreed the declaration, they represent an 'international Magna Carta for all men everywhere'. However, cultural relativists, such as Edward Said (*Orientalism*, 1978), associate a universalist approach to human rights with Western cultural imperialism. This is because they argue that one's human rights are determined by social and religious factors. For example, Asian values (as encapsulated by the 1993 Bangkok Declaration) emphasise the well-being of society over the individual. This is also the case with Confucian values in China, so both these world views conflict with the Western focus on the individual. The secular basis of a universalist approach to human rights also conflicts with religions such as Islam, which claim that the supreme definition of human rights derives from divine revelation in the Qur'an. Similarly, the Orthodox Church possesses highly conservative social views which strongly conflict with the focus on individual self-determination in the Universal Declaration of Human Rights.

> **A01** This answer is well rooted in wide-ranging and impressive detail.

> **A02** The way in which the candidate so clearly explains the arguments in favour of a universalist approach and then provides equally strong coverage of criticism of it ensures a strong showing at A02. No A03 evaluation is required by the question, so the candidate is right not to judge whether a universalist approach to human rights is justified.

6   How successful have the four UN tribunals been?   4 marks

Worked example

Four UN tribunals have been established to try war crimes, crimes against humanity and genocide, in Rwanda, the former Yugoslavia, Sierra Leone and Cambodia. All of them have secured important convictions and some have established important new principles in international law.

> **A01** This suggests considerable knowledge of all four tribunals.

The tribunal for the former Yugoslavia secured an impressive 90 convictions including the Bosnian Serb leaders Radovan Karadzic and Ratko Mladic who were both held responsible for the Srebrenica massacre in 1995. However, it has been less effective in encouraging reconciliation in the Balkans because Serbia (backed by Russia) has claimed that it represents victors' justice. The tribunal for Sierra Leone convicted a former head of state, Charles Taylor, for war crimes, which sets an important precedent that heads of government are not protected by state sovereignty when abusing the human rights of their citizens. It also established the principle that the use of child soldiers was a crime against humanity, although critics claim that its funding by the West has undermined its legitimacy. The tribunal for Rwanda also set the important new precedent in international law that rape can be used with genocidal intent and that the media can be held legally responsible for encouraging genocide. However, it has also been criticised for securing relatively few convictions, given the scale of the killing, and for failing to investigate subsequent atrocities carried out by Tutsis against Hutus. The tribunal for Cambodia has been successful in convicting three notorious leaders of the Khmer Rouge regime for carrying out genocidal policies (including Nuon Chea, the chief ideologist of the Khmer Rouge). However, critics claim that, given the scale of the killing, the court succeeded in bringing only very few people

> **A02** The candidate explains what all of them have achieved.

to justice. Therefore, this suggests that none of the tribunals has been completely successful, since they have not always achieved reconciliation and only achieved partial justice for the victims. However, they have all been important in advancing the principle of international human rights-based law and by convicting a number of infamous criminals have achieved at least some degree of justice for the bereaved.

> AO3 The extent to which criticisms of each tribunal mean that they have been unsuccessful is explored throughout, leading to a substantiated judgement.

7   To what extent can the International Court of Justice claim to be a successful organisation?

4 marks

....

....

....

8   Is it fair to say that the failures of the International Criminal Court outweigh its successes?

4 marks

....

....

....

Why is it difficult to enforce a universal standard of human rights?

Although several institutions have been established to enforce an international standard of human rights, their success has been mixed. This is because nation states are sovereign and so often fail to support the work of international courts and tribunals. The diverse ways in which different cultures and religions define human rights further undermine attempts to establish a universal standard of global human rights protection.

Practice questions ?

AO1 Knowledge and understanding

9   In what ways does state sovereignty challenge the effectiveness of international courts and tribunals?

2 marks

....

....

10 What is the difference between a universalist and a cultural relativist approach to human rights?

2 marks

....

....

11 Why are realists sceptical of attempts to establish a global standard of human rights protection?

2 marks

....

....

12 Explain why liberals believe that human rights abuses should not be tolerated by the international community.

2 marks

....

....

AO2 and AO3 Analysis and evaluation

13 Why do some nation states support a liberal approach to global human rights protection more than others?

4 marks

....

....

....

....

14 In what ways is there a clash between universal human rights and state sovereignty?

4 marks

....

....

....

....

15 Is it fair to state that the ongoing importance of state sovereignty makes it impossible to establish a supranational standard of human rights protection?

4 marks

....

....

....

....

16 Have human rights become better protected since the end of the Cold War in 1991?

4 marks

....

....

....

....

Why did humanitarian interventions increase during the 1990s and in which circumstances have they been most successful?

When the geo-strategic rivalries of the Cold War ended in 1991, liberals hoped that a new world order based upon a universal standard of human rights protection could be established. A number of successful humanitarian interventions took place in Bosnia, Kosovo and East Timor, which indicated a new emphasis on human rights protection. However, failed interventions in Somalia, Libya and Afghanistan demonstrate that practical as well as moral considerations need to be taken into account when planning an intervention.

Practice questions ?

AO1 Knowledge and understanding

17 Why did humanitarian interventions increase during the 1990s?   2 marks

....

....

18 Why did NATO intervene in Bosnia (1995) and in Kosovo (1999)?   2 marks

....

....

19 What is the significance of Tony Blair's Chicago speech (1999)?   2 marks

....

....

20 What is 'nation building' and how does it encourage a successful humanitarian intervention?   2 marks

....

....

AO2 and AO3 Analysis and evaluation

21 Why do you think the US intervention in Somalia in 1992 was so much less successful than the NATO intervention in Bosnia in 1995?   4 marks

....

....

....

....

....

....

22 Do you think that international intervention in Myanmar on behalf of the
Rohingya Muslims could ever be justified? **4 marks**

....

....

....

....

23 Why did the humanitarian intervention in Libya go so disastrously wrong? **4 marks**

....

....

....

....

24 Does the fact that Western powers are currently the only ones to launch
humanitarian interventions undermine their legitimacy? **4 marks**

....

....

....

....

The reasons for selective interventions and the extent to which humanitarian interventions are justified

In 2005 the United Nations World Summit endorsed 'Responsibility to Protect'. This
established the principle that outside powers can intervene within nation states if
significant human rights abuses are taking place. However, the way in which the
UN's Responsibility to Protect makes sovereignty conditional upon the protection
of human rights is highly controversial. The way in which Western powers have only
selectively intervened in humanitarian crises has also fuelled claims of hypocrisy
and double standards.

Practice questions ?

AO1 Knowledge and understanding

25 Under what circumstances does UN Responsibility to Protect claim that the
international community may intervene within a sovereign nation state? **2 marks**

....

....

26 Why do realists and liberals regard UN Responsibility to Protect so differently?   2 marks

....

....

27 Explain the accusation of double standards in the context of humanitarian intervention.   2 marks

....

....

28 Why have there been fewer humanitarian interventions in recent years?   2 marks

....

....

AO2 and AO3 Analysis and evaluation

29 Why do you think the decision of Western powers to avoid large-scale humanitarian intervention in the Syrian civil war has been so controversial?   4 marks

....

....

....

....

30 Do you agree that the accusation of double standards undermines the case for humanitarian intervention?   4 marks

....

....

....

....

31 Is it true that humanitarian intervention is now an 'abandoned project?'   4 marks

....

....

....

32 Since humanitarian interventions have generally been directed at less powerful nation states by more powerful ones, does this undermine their legitimacy?   4 marks

....

....

....

Role and significance of global civil society and non-state actors in protecting human rights

Global awareness of the importance of human rights has been significantly increased by the United Nations and by global pressure groups such as Human Rights Watch. The way in which the internet can create instant global awareness of human rights violations has further advanced international debate about human rights. The internet can also enable mass movements to mobilise in support of human rights, as seen with the international reach of the Black Lives Matter movement.

Practice questions ?

AO1 Knowledge and understanding

33 In what ways does Human Rights Watch raise awareness of human rights abuses?   2 marks

....

....

34 Why is there now greater global awareness of the plight of the Uighur Muslims in China?   2 marks

....

....

35 In what ways is the role of the United Nations High Commissioner for Human Rights limited?   2 marks

....

....

36 In what ways can social media advance global awareness of human rights abuses?   2 marks

....

AO2 and AO3 Analysis and evaluation

37 How much progress do you think global pressure groups have made in protecting human rights?   4 marks

....

....

....

38 To what extent does negative publicity encourage nation states to better protect human rights?   4 marks

....

....

....

39 What are the main criticisms of the United Nations Human Rights Council and how valid are they? 4 marks

....

....

....

....

40 Do you think that mass protest is significant in encouraging governments not to abuse human rights? 4 marks

....

....

....

....

Paper 3 Section A

1 Examine the main weaknesses of the European Court of Human Rights and the International Court of Justice. 12 marks

Write a plan here, then use a separate sheet of paper to answer the question in full. **15**

....

....

....

....

....

....

....

2 Examine the reasons why some humanitarian interventions have proved more successful than others. 12 marks

Write a plan here, then use a separate sheet of paper to answer the question in full. **15**

....

....

....

....

....

....

....

....

....

....

Paper 3 Section C

3 Evaluate the extent to which the importance of state sovereignty undermines
   all attempts to improve global human rights protection.   **30 marks**

Write a plan here, then use a separate sheet of paper to answer the question in full.

(45)

....

....

....

....

....

....

....

....

....

4 Evaluate the extent to which the changing balance of global power is making it
   impossible to enforce a global standard of human rights protection.   **30 marks**

Write a plan here, then use a separate sheet of paper to answer the question in full.

(45)

....

....

....

....

....

....

....

....

5 Evaluate the extent to which the claim of double standards undermines the case for humanitarian intervention.

30 marks

Write a plan here, then use a separate sheet of paper to answer the question in full.

45

....

....

....

....

....

....

....

....

6 Evaluate the extent to which only humanitarian interventions supported by the United Nations are justifiable.

30 marks

Write a plan here, then use a separate sheet of paper to answer the question in full.

45

....

....

....

....

....

....

....

....

7 Evaluate the extent to which humanitarian interventions encourage or discourage stability.

30 marks

Write a plan here, then use a separate sheet of paper to answer the question in full.

45

....

....

....

....

....

....

....

Topic 6 Global governance: environmental

Competing views about how to tackle climate change

There are considerable differences over the issue of climate change. 'Deep green' (radical) ecology is planet-centred. Human beings have an obligation to protect the planet because it sustains and nurtures all life. In order to do this, capitalism must be abandoned in favour of other less exploitative economic systems. 'Shallow green' (reformist) ecology is human-centred. It is more pragmatic and is the idea that environmental preservation should protect human interests. This can be achieved within the existing capitalistic system. Progress in achieving sustainable development (meeting the needs of the present without compromising the needs of future generations) is made difficult by the way in which nation states generally prioritise their immediate economic advantage over the well-being of all (the tragedy of the commons).

Practice questions ?

AO1 Knowledge and understanding

1 What is deep green (radical) ecology? 2 marks

2 What is shallow green (reformist) ecology? 2 marks

3 Explain the meaning of sustainable development. 2 marks

4 Explain the significance of the tragedy of the commons. 2 marks

AO2 and AO3 Analysis and evaluation

5 Why and with what significance do nation states favour shallow green (reformist) over deep green (radical) ecology? 4 marks

Worked example

Nation states favour shallow green (reformist) approaches to climate change because they do not require a complete transformation of capitalism and the free market. The changes required by shallow green ecology, such as transferring to green energy, encouraging public transport and discouraging waste, can all be achieved within existing economic and political structures. Strong economic growth rates are also possible within a shallow green context and there are also likely to be strong investment opportunities as the free market adapts to new technology such as electric cars. The public will also not be expected to change their consumer habits radically, which makes a shallow green approach to environmental issues relatively uncontroversial to implement, so nation states favour them.

> AO1 The nature and attractions of a shallow green ecological approach are clearly understood and explained.

A deep green ecological strategy would be much more difficult for governments to enforce because it would place considerable restraints on people's freedoms. For example, a deep green approach to climate change might include limits on, for example, flying, meat eating and car ownership. The way, too, in which green ecology favours zero economic growth to achieve complete sustainability would mean a total transformation of the way in which the free market operates, which no government would be likely to implement. Critics claim, with some justification, that although nation states' preference for reformist ecology is understandable, it makes it significantly more difficult to limit temperature rise. For example, if nation states do not take more urgent action, the Intergovernmental Panel on Climate Change (IPCC) predicts that temperature rise during the twenty-first century is likely to be 3°C rather than the 1.5°C recommended by the Paris Treaty in 2015.

> AO2 The reasons why nation states prefer the shallow green approach to a deep green ecological approach are clearly explained and the possible consequences of this are explored. No AO3 evaluation is required.

6   To what extent do you think that the principles of the tragedy of the commons make effective progress on resolving the problem of climate change impossible?   4 marks

Worked example

According to Garrett Hardin, an ecologist, the tragedy of the commons theory explains why progress on resolving the problem of climate change has been limited. This is because nation states selfishly prioritise their own short-term economic advantage over the well-being of the global community. As Hardin puts it, 'freedom in a commons brings ruin to all'. The failure of nation states each to make sacrifices to cut their carbon emissions therefore explains why progress at climate change conferences has been so limited. For example, the Rio de Janeiro (1992) and Kyoto (1997) conferences failed to achieve substantial progress because leading members of the developed world, led by the USA, felt that they were being required to put greater limits on their carbon emissions than the developing world was. Therefore, they refused to commit to cutting their carbon emissions in order to protect their economies. Even though the Paris conference (2015) is generally seen as more successful, nation states were still unprepared to accept mandatory cuts on their carbon emissions for the good of the 'global commons'. However, there is growing evidence from the Intergovernmental Panel on Climate Change that the global temperature rise this century is likely to be 3°C with disastrous consequences for the planet. Such shocking evidence may encourage nation states to decide that the long-term well-being of the planet outweighs short-term economic challenges. The UK, for

> AO1 The response benefits from a crisp understanding of the meaning of the tragedy of the commons thesis supported by helpful detail.

> AO2 The candidate then sensibly contextualises the theory within climate change conferences.

example, has increased its carbon-cutting commitment to 68% of 1990 levels by 2030 and the European Union has increased its commitment from 40% to 55% cuts by 2030. These more ambitious targets indicate that it is still possible for nation states to avoid a tragedy of the commons if they recognise that climate change is a shared dilemma which requires immediate collective action.

> AO3 The way in which the candidate questions the extent to which the tragedy of the commons thesis provides a complete picture of the action being taken on climate change ensures that AO3 evaluation is achieved.

7 Why are deep green (radical) ecologists so critical of shallow green (reformist) ecology?

4 marks

....

....

....

8 How widely is it accepted that development must now be sustainable?

4 marks

....

....

....

Role and significance of the United Nations Framework Convention on Climate Change and the Intergovernmental Panel on Climate Change

In 1988, the United Nations Intergovernmental Panel on Climate Change (IPCC) was established to provide scientific data on the way in which the climate is changing. In 1992, the United Nations Framework Convention on Climate Change (UNFCCC) was agreed at the Rio de Janeiro summit. Its aim is to encourage nation states to cooperate to reduce carbon emissions in order to protect the environment. To facilitate this the UNFCCC provides a forum in which nation states come together at regular conferences to discuss ways of reducing their carbon emissions.

Practice questions ?

AO1 Knowledge and understanding

9 What is the purpose and significance of the IPCC?

2 marks

....

....

10 What is the significance of the UNFCCC?

2 marks

....

....

11 What does the IPCC recommend as the maximum allowable temperature increase in the twenty-first century? 2 marks

....

....

12 Explain the meaning of Conference of the Parties (COP). 2 marks

....

....

AO2 and AO3 Analysis and evaluation

13 What is the main achievement of the IPCC? 4 marks

....

....

....

....

14 What are the main problems that the IPCC faces? 4 marks

....

....

....

....

....

15 What are the main successes of the UNFCCC? 4 marks

....

....

....

....

....

16 What stops the UNFCCC from being more successful? 4 marks

....

....

....

....

....

Strengths and weaknesses of climate change conferences

There have been four climate change conferences which have played a significant role in establishing the nature and extent of the global response to climate change. These are Rio de Janeiro (1992), Kyoto (1997), Copenhagen (2009) and Paris (2015). Each of the resulting treaties brought the issue of climate change important international publicity. However, the effectiveness of the conferences has often been undermined by state sovereignty and self-interest, as well as by tension between the developing and the developed world over measurement and responsibility.

Practice questions ?

AO1 Knowledge and understanding

17 In what ways did the Rio de Janeiro (1992) conference make important progress on resolving the issue of climate change? 2 marks

....

....

18 Why was the developed world often critical of the Rio de Janeiro (1992) and Kyoto (1997) conferences? 2 marks

....

....

19 What were the main successes and failures of the Copenhagen conference (2009)? 2 marks

....

....

20 Explain the Intended Nationally Determined Contributions (INDCs) agreed at the Paris conference (2015). 2 marks

....

....

AO2 and AO3 Analysis and evaluation

21 Since no climate change conference has imposed binding targets on nation states' carbon emissions, do you think that they have all been failures? 4 marks

....

....

....

....

....

....

22 Do you think that the Paris conference (2015) was a success or a failure?　4 marks

....

....

....

....

23 How important is cooperation between China and the USA in resolving the challenge of climate change and why is it difficult to achieve?　4 marks

....

....

....

....

24 To what extent and why has conflict between the developed and the developing world undermined the effectiveness of climate change conferences?　4 marks

....

....

....

....

Role and significance of global civil society and non-state actors in climate change

Although nation states play a vital role in determining the global response to climate change, global civil society and non-state actors are also increasingly important in publicising the issue and suggesting solutions. These include individual activists, international entrepreneurs, research institutes, global foundations, cities and elected mayors.

Practice questions ?

AO1 Knowledge and understanding

25 Explain the importance of Greta Thunberg and one other activist.　2 marks

....

....

26 What is the significance of the C40 Cities Climate Leadership Group?　2 marks

....

....

Paper 3 Section C

3   Evaluate the extent to which significant progress is being made to address the challenge of climate change.

30 marks

Write a plan here, then use a separate sheet of paper to answer the question in full.

45

....

....

....

....

....

....

....

....

4   Evaluate the extent to which climate change conferences have made little progress in resolving the problem of climate change.

30 marks

Write a plan here, then use a separate sheet of paper to answer the question in full.

45

....

....

....

....

....

....

....

5   Evaluate the extent to which non-state actors play as important a role in resolving the problem of climate change as nation states do.

30 marks

Write a plan here, then use a separate sheet of paper to answer the question in full.

45

....

....

....

....

....

....

....

6 Evaluate the extent to which tension between the developed and the developing world has meant that insufficient progress has been made to resolve the issue of climate change.

30 marks

Write a plan here, then use a separate sheet of paper to answer the question in full.

....

....

....

....

....

....

....

....

....

....

....

7 Evaluate the extent to which effective action on climate change requires nation states to accept mandatory limits on their carbon emissions.

30 marks

Write a plan here, then use a separate sheet of paper to answer the question in full.

....

....

....

....

....

....

....

....

....

....

....

Topic 7 Power and developments

Different types of power

Power means the ability to influence others in a certain direction. The political scientist Joseph Nye coined the terms 'hard power' and 'soft power'. Hard power is generally associated with military and economic compulsion. Soft power is associated with cultural and diplomatic persuasion. The forms of soft power (persuasion) and hard power (compulsion) being exercised in international relations provide two contrasting ways in which nation states can achieve their objectives.

Practice questions (?)

AO1 Knowledge and understanding

1 Explain the meaning of soft power.   2 marks

....

....

2 Explain the meaning of hard power.   2 marks

....

....

3 Provide an example of the USA using hard power and an example of it using soft power to achieve its objectives.   2 marks

....

....

4 Provide an example of China using hard power and an example of it using soft power to achieve its objectives.   2 marks

....

....

AO2 and AO3 Analysis and evaluation

5 Why do realists favour hard power over soft power?   4 marks

Worked example

According to realism, nation states, like human beings, possess predatory instincts and seek to achieve power and influence for themselves. Since nation states are 'power maximisers' and because there is no supranational authority able to impose order, sovereign states must ensure their own security in an unstable and constantly threatening world order. The best method for securing survival is hard power because building a strong military is the most effective way of deterring the aggression of potential rivals. For example, NATO carries out regular military exercises in order to deter Russia from launching an attack on one of its members and in 2020 the UK committed to a significant increase in military spending to safeguard British interests.

A strong military capability can also compel other nation states to act in a certain way. China, for example, is extending its military influence in its neighbourhood by militarising reefs to convince the USA that it should recognise Chinese regional hegemony in the South China Sea. Realists therefore regard the calculated use of military power as much more effective than soft power because it provides the most effective way of compelling others to act in a certain way. Soft power is much less tangible. For example, the European Union's commitment to human rights, democracy and environmental activism means it has a great deal of international prestige and cultural attractiveness among other liberal democracies. However, its lack of military power means that it is often marginalised in global crises and it has no military deterrent power against Russia. Given the constant threats to a nation state's security in an anarchic world order in which there is no 'night watchman' (John Mearsheimer), realists therefore view hard power as a much more immediate and powerful force than soft power. As Otto von Bismarck, one of the great nineteenth-century realist statesmen, put it, 'A conquering army on the border will not be stopped by eloquence.'

> **A01** This response neatly connects realism to the advantages of hard power. The supporting evidence is relevant and is clearly deployed to answer the question.

> **A02** The advantages of hard power and the limitations of soft power in terms of realism are confidently analysed. A03 evaluation is not required.

6   To what extent do you think that to be a superpower a nation state requires both hard and soft power global influence?

4 marks

Worked example

The USA possesses the hard and soft power influence that enables its influence to be felt globally. Militarily, it has unrivalled outreach with 800 military bases around the world. It also wields huge economic influence as the world's biggest economy, as the dollar is the world's reserve currency. However, the USA's influence is also so far-reaching because of the considerable appeal of US culture. Hollywood is a globally dominant brand and US companies such as McDonald's, Apple, Google and Facebook ensure that US free market commercial values have a global following. This cultural appeal has enabled the USA to exercise huge world influence. For example, one of the key reasons why the Cold War ended in 1991 was that the Soviet Union could not ideologically compete with US consumer values. The USA has therefore been able to extend its influence so widely because of the combination of its economic and military hard power and its unrivalled cultural outreach, which has made other countries so eager to emulate the American way of life.

> **A01** The knowledge of how both the USA and China (in the next paragraph) exert influence is detailed and appropriate.

> **A02** In both cases, the implications of the evidence are clearly explained with constant analytical focus on how the power of the USA and China enables them to exert influence.

In spite of the establishment of some overseas Confucius Institutes, China lacks comparative soft power cultural outreach. However, it has growing hard power influence, which many realists argue already makes it a superpower. Its economy has grown dramatically to rival that of the USA and the establishment of both the Asia Infrastructure Bank and the Belt and Road Initiative is designed to make China the dominant force in the global economy. Indeed, China's economic influence in the developing world now makes it the world's most powerful neo-colonial power and it is already the dominant outside influence in Africa. In addition, its growing military outreach is already challenging US power in the South China Sea. This has all been achieved with comparatively little focus on the cultural appeal of China, which suggests that economic and military hard power may be enough to be a superpower. Chinese values may, therefore, lack a universal following but the power of Chinese investment backed by growing military self-confidence seem likely to be sufficient for China to achieve the necessary global outreach to claim superpower status.

> AO3 The confident way in which the candidate then questions the utility of soft power in achieving superpower status ensures a very strong AO3 performance.

7 To what extent can it be argued that the internet has made soft power more important in global relations?

4 marks

....

....

....

8 Do you think the USA's use of hard power and soft power were equally important in ending the Cold War?

4 marks

....

....

....

....

Differing significance of states in global affairs and the classification of state power

When the Cold War ended in 1991, the USA could claim to be the world's only superpower. This is because it was the only state able to exert its influence anywhere in the world. Great powers possess significant economic, military, diplomatic and regional power but cannot wield the same sort of global influence. However, the extent to which the USA's power remains dominant and unrivalled is now in question as a result of the rise of China and other emerging powers, such as Russia, Brazil, India, South Africa, Iran and Turkey.

Practice questions ?

AO1 Knowledge and understanding

9 Define the term 'superpower'.

2 marks

....

....

10 Define the term 'great power'.

2 marks

....

....

11 Explain why the USA is a superpower.

2 marks

....

....

12 Define the term 'emerging power'.

2 marks

....

....

AO2 and AO3 Analysis and evaluation

13 Why are the UK and Russia great powers rather than superpowers?

4 marks

....

....

....

....

14 Why are India and Brazil often defined as emerging powers?

4 marks

....

....

....

....

15 What are the arguments for and against China being a superpower?

4 marks

....

....

....

....

16 To what extent has Russia's lack of soft power influence reduced its global influence?

4 marks

....

....

....

....

The consequences for global stability of the various types of polar structures of power

When one power is dominant, international relations are referred to as being unipolar. The dominant power is then referred to as the global hegemon. When two superpowers contest influence, the distribution is bipolar. This was the case during the Cold War. When a number of nation states possesses similar power, the result is a multipolar distribution of power. Each one of these possible distributions of power has significant consequences for global order and stability. Realists favour a bipolar or a unipolar distribution of power because of the greater uncertainty involved in a multipolar distribution of power.

Practice questions ?

AO1 Knowledge and understanding

17 Define the term 'bipolarity'. 2 marks

....

....

18 Why is the Cold War a good example of a bipolar distribution of power? 2 marks

....

....

19 What is the connection between unipolarity and global hegemony? 2 marks

....

....

20 Explain the meaning of a multipolar distribution of global power. 2 marks

....

....

AO2 and AO3 Analysis and evaluation

21 In what circumstances is multipolarity most likely to encourage peace and stability? 4 marks

....

....

....

....

22 How convincing is the argument that a bipolar distribution of power contributes to peace and stability? 4 marks

....

....

....

23 What is hegemonic stability theory and why is it contested? 4 marks

....

....

....

....

24 Do you think that global relations are now becoming multipolar? 4 marks

....

....

....

....

The characteristics of different systems of government and their consequences for global order

The governments of nation states can be democratic, semi-democratic, non-democratic or autocratic. Liberals generally view democracies as most likely to encourage peace and stability because of their commitment to human rights and the rule of law. Realists respond that all nation states are power maximisers and so the way in which they are governed is irrelevant to global stability. Failed states are states where government has collapsed. These can destabilise a region because they can become prey to criminal gangs, terrorists and neighbouring powers. Rogue states are states which do not act according to recognised global standards of behaviour. However, the subjectivity of the term makes it controversial.

Practice questions ?

AO1 Knowledge and understanding

25 How is a democratic state different from an autocratic state? 2 marks

....

....

26 What is a failed state and why are they often seen as a threat to peace and stability? 2 marks

....

....

27 What is a rogue state and why can they be viewed as a threat to peace and stability? 2 marks

....

....

28 Why is Russia a semi-democratic state and why might this matter in global relations? 2 marks

....

....

AO2 and AO3 Analysis and evaluation

29 Is it fair to state that democratic governments are less likely to provoke war
   than semi-autocratic and autocratic governments? 4 marks

....

....

....

....

30 To what extent are North Korea and Iran justly viewed as rogue states? 4 marks

....

....

....

....

31 Research two failed states. To what extent have they been a threat to regional
   peace and stability? 4 marks

....

....

....

32 Do you think that the term 'rogue state' is a helpful one? 4 marks

....

....

....

The impact of the changing balance of power on contemporary global issues

Since 2000 the hegemonic power of the USA has been challenged by the rise of emerging powers, most notably China. Emerging powers have lifted millions out of extreme poverty, so helping to tackle this problem. However, the shift in the balance of power creates the potential for conflict and the authoritarian nature of a number of emerging powers is likely to have a negative impact on human rights protection. The rapid growth of emerging powers has also led to greater carbon emissions by the developing world, making it more difficult to resolve the problem of climate change.

AO1 Knowledge and understanding

33 Explain two ways in which China is now challenging the USA's global influence.   2 marks

....

....

34 In what ways can the European Union be viewed as an emerging power?   2 marks

....

....

35 What do you understand by the term 'power transition' and why can such a
period be destabilising?   2 marks

....

....

36 Why have tensions increased between India and China in recent years?   2 marks

....

....

AO2 and AO3 Analysis and evaluation

37 Why might the changing balance of global power impact negatively on
human rights protection?   4 marks

....

....

....

38 In what ways is the USA still acting as a global hegemon?   4 marks

....

....

....

39 To what extent is US military hegemony being challenged?   4 marks

....

....

....

....

40 Do you think that the rise of emerging powers has been positive or negative? **4 marks**

....

....

....

....

Exam-style questions **?**

Paper 3 Section A

1 Examine the main reasons why rogue states and failed states are often seen as a threat to global peace and stability. **12 marks**

Write a plan here, then use a separate sheet of paper to answer the question in full.

15

....

....

....

....

....

....

....

....

....

....

2 Examine the main ways in which China and the USA exert global influence. **12 marks**

Write a plan here, then use a separate sheet of paper to answer the question in full.

15

....

....

....

....

....

....

....

....

....

Paper 3 Section C

3 Evaluate the extent to which the rise of emerging powers means that the USA can no longer claim to be world hegemon. **30 marks**

Write a plan here, then use a separate sheet of paper to answer the question in full.

45

....

....

....

....

....

....

....

....

4 Evaluate the extent to which soft power is significantly less important in international relations than hard power. **30 marks**

Write a plan here, then use a separate sheet of paper to answer the question in full.

45

....

....

....

....

....

....

....

....

5 Evaluate the extent to which a unipolar distribution of global power is more likely to achieve stability than a bipolar distribution of global power. **30 marks**

Write a plan here, then use a separate sheet of paper to answer the question in full.

45

....

....

....

....

Workbook answers at **www.hoddereducation.co.uk/workbookanswers**

....

....

....

....

....

6 Evaluate the extent to which the policies of semi-autocratic and autocratic governments are more likely to lead to conflict than the policies of democracies. **30 marks**

Write a plan here, then use a separate sheet of paper to answer the question in full.

45

....

....

....

....

....

....

....

....

....

....

7 Evaluate the extent to which failed states pose a greater threat to regional and global stability than rogue states. **30 marks**

Write a plan here, then use a separate sheet of paper to answer the question in full.

45

....

....

....

....

....

....

....

....

Topic 8 Regionalism and the European Union

The different forms of regionalism

Nation states choose to join regional organisations for diverse reasons. This can be to encourage prosperity by fostering closer trading relations between the member states and to take better advantage of the opportunities offered by globalisation. It can also be to provide nation states with increased global influence or to increase their regional security. Some regional organisations like the European Union (EU) have developed state-like characteristics. However, others such as the Arab League are much less unified. Nation states which join regional bodies to a greater or lesser extent sacrifice sovereignty in order to share in the collective benefits of membership.

Practice questions ?

AO1 Knowledge and understanding

1 Explain the meaning of economic globalisation.   2 marks

....

....

2 Explain the meaning of political globalisation.   2 marks

....

....

3 In what ways does the EU combine economic, political and security regionalism?   2 marks

....

....

4 Explain the connection between regionalism and globalisation.   2 marks

....

....

AO2 and AO3 Analysis and evaluation

5 To what extent do regional organisations impact differently on the sovereignty of their member states?   4 marks

Worked example

The purpose with which they were established explains why regional bodies impact differently on the sovereignty of their member states. The EEC/EU was established as a response to the nationalism that provoked the two world wars which devastated Europe. Its purpose of 'ever closer union' (Rome, 1957) was consequently designed to create a more integrated Europe. The EU's supranational institutions of governance, such as the European Commission, the European Court of Justice and the European Central Bank, therefore establish an authority greater than the nation state.

AO1 Clear knowledge of regional organisations: the EU, Arab League, NAFTA/ USMCA, African Union and ASEAN (next paragraph). The breadth of knowledge adds to the conviction of the response.

AO2 There is a clear analysis here and in the next paragraph of the ways in which they impact differently on the sovereignty of their members.

Other regional organisations have gone less far in challenging the sovereignty of their members. The Arab League is simply designed to encourage dialogue between member states and to represent Arab interests on the world stage. Its member states do not therefore accept limits on their sovereignty and each member state possesses a veto over policy. As an economic example of regionalism, the North American Free Trade Agreement (NAFTA)/United States–Mexico–Canada Agreement (USMCA) does commit its member states to accepting certain economic and environmental rules of engagement, but since it has no higher political purpose its impact on sovereignty is limited. Both the African Union and the Association of Southeast Asian Nations (ASEAN) aspire to greater integration. For example, ASEAN encourages free trade between its members and in 2021 the African Continental Free Trade Area opened. However, both are founded on the principle of the sovereign independence of their members, rather than the European principle of 'ever closer union'. This means that, even though they favour some degree of integration, their impact on the sovereignty of their member states is considerably less than that of the EU.

> **A03** A clear exploration of how the reasons for their creation determines the extent to which they impact on national sovereignty ensures strong evaluative focus.

6   How much foreign policy influence do regional bodies possess?   **4 marks**

Worked example

Although all regional bodies provide opportunities for collective decision making, their impact in global relations is very different. Without doubt the European Union (EU) possesses the most global influence. This is because the Maastricht Treaty (1993) established the principle of a common foreign and defence policy and the Lisbon Treaty (2009) provided the EU with a legal identity so that its President and High Commissioner for Foreign Affairs can negotiate with nation states on behalf of its members. For example, the EU is a full member of the World Trade Organization (WTO), deploying its considerable economic power to negotiate favourable trade deals on behalf of its members. It has also represented its members at the Paris Treaty in 2015 and is a member of the G20. However, EU foreign and defence policy is still subject to the veto, which makes it difficult for the EU to agree on a unified approach to contentious foreign policy issues such as the Syrian civil war and tensions between Ukraine and Russia. As a result, the impact of the EU in global diplomacy is significantly reduced. However, the EU still possesses more global influence than other regional organisations which are primarily intergovernmental and so lack the necessary cohesion to be as globally influential. For example, the Arab League's lack of economic integration means that it cannot deploy the same sort of hard power that the EU can in global relations. Its members are also so committed to their sovereignty that they are unwilling to commit military resources to the proposed Joint Arab Force. The African Union's Peace and Security Council

> **A01** Strong evidence is supplied throughout the answer about a number of regional organisations: the EU, Arab League, Arican Union and ASEAN. The candidate avoids the trap of focusing too much on the EU when the question is much broader.

authorises the African Union to deploy peace-keepers within conflict zones such as Mali and the Central African Republic. However, the African Union's global influence is minimal because it is not represented on any institutions of global governance and, like the Arab League, lacks economic hard power. ASEAN is similarly diplomatically weak because its members make their own foreign policy decisions. Cambodia and Myanmar, for example, are closely linked to China, while the Philippines is aligned with the United States. This makes it very difficult to achieve a collective response to problems such as China's expansionism in the South China Sea. This therefore suggests that the EU is the only regional organisation with significant global influence, although even the EU's global influence is minimal, since foreign policy and defence are still subject to the national veto.

> **AO2** Detailed knowledge of the aims and structure of the various regional bodies is used to explain their relative impact.

> **AO3** The way in which the greater influence of the EU is contrasted with other regional organisations provides strong evaluative focus. Questioning the EU's foreign policy influence further accesses evaluative marks.

7 Does the EU provide a model for other regional organisations? **4 marks**

....
....
....
....
....

8 To what extent do all regional bodies pursue the same objectives? **4 marks**

....
....
....
....
....

Development of regional organisations, excluding the EU

The Arab League is essentially designed to provide Arab nation states with greater diplomatic influence in international diplomacy. The North American Free Trade Agreement (NAFTA), which has been renegotiated as the United States–Mexico–Canada Agreement (USMCA), is designed to increase trade between its members. The Association of Southeast Asian Nations (ASEAN) goes further by encouraging free trade and promoting peace and security between its members. The African Union was established to encourage greater economic, social and political links between its members and to safeguard their independence from colonial exploitation.

AO1 Knowledge and understanding questions

9 In what ways is the Arab League an example of political regionalism?   2 marks

....

....

10 In what ways is NAFTA/USMCA an example of economic regionalism?   2 marks

....

....

11 What are the main aims of ASEAN?   2 marks

....

....

12 Why is the African Union an example of both political and economic regionalism?   2 marks

....

....

AO2 and AO3 Analysis and evaluation

13 Why has the 'ASEAN Way' been criticised?   4 marks

....

....

....

....

14 How similar is ASEAN to the European Union?   4 marks

....

....

....

....

15 What have been the most important reasons why the African Union has found it
   difficult to achieve greater economic and political union?   4 marks

....

....

....

....

....

16 To what extent do you think the Arab League is a failed regional organisation? **4 marks**

....

....

....

....

....

Factors that have fostered European integration and the major developments through which this has occurred

The European Union (EU) is the most advanced regional body in the world. The Treaty of Rome established the European Economic Community (EEC) in 1957. Since then successive treaties have encouraged 'ever closer union' between its member states. In 1993, the Treaty of Maastricht took this process further by establishing the EU based upon the economic and monetary union of its members. The EEC/EU has significantly expanded from six members (1957) to 27 members (2021). There is still significant debate over the extent to which the government of the EU should be supranational or intergovernmental.

Practice questions ?

AO1 Knowledge and understanding

17 Within the context of the EU, explain the meaning and significance of the term 'ever closer union'. **2 marks**

....

....

18 Why is the Maastricht Treaty (1993) so important in the development of the EU? **2 marks**

....

....

19 Explain 'widening and deepening' within the context of the EU. **2 marks**

....

....

20 Explain the meaning and significance of the terms 'supranational' and 'intergovernmental' within the context of the EU. **2 marks**

....

....

AO2 and AO3 Analysis and evaluation

21 To what extent do you think that the EU has succeeded in creating 'ever closer union' between its member states? **4 marks**

....

....

....

....

22 Why and with what justification has it been suggested that it is difficult for the EU to broaden and deepen at the same time? **4 marks**

....

....

....

....

23 To what extent did the Lisbon Treaty (2009) lead to further integration within the EU? **4 marks**

....

....

....

....

24 Why is there so much tension between supranationalism and intergovernmentalism in terms of the future of the EU? **4 marks**

....

....

....

....

Significance of the EU as an international body/global actor

The Maastricht Treaty (1993) established a common foreign and security policy for the EU. Given the tremendous size of its economy, the EU also wields significant economic power in global relations. Membership of important intergovernmental organisations such as the World Trade Organization also provides the EU with structural power. However, without an army the EU lacks military power, and since foreign and defence policy is still subject to the national veto, it is often difficult to establish a united and coherent EU policy.

AO1 Knowledge and understanding

25 Explain two ways in which the EU exerts economic influence. **2 marks**

26 Compare the role that the EU plays in the World Trade Organization and in the United Nations. **2 marks**

27 In what ways has the EU responded to the Syrian civil war? **2 marks**

28 In what ways has the EU provided global leadership in terms of climate change? **2 marks**

AO2 and AO3 Analysis and evaluation

29 Why has the EU found it so difficult establishing a unified response to Russia? **4 marks**

30 To what extent do you think that the national veto over foreign and defence policy is the main reason why the EU lacks global influence? **4 marks**

31 Do you agree that the EU's lack of military power makes it irrelevant in terms of global influence? **4 marks**

32 Contrast the EU's effectiveness in its dealings with Russia and Iran. 4 marks

....

....

....

....

....

The ways in and extent to which regionalism addresses and resolves contemporary global issues

Different regional bodies approach global problems in diverse ways. The EU is, for example, uniquely committed to advancing human rights. It has also made significant steps in environmental protection in a way that other regional bodies have not attempted. Both the EU and the African Union have committed troops to conflict resolution. The way in which ASEAN has encouraged trade liberalisation between its members has helped to alleviate poverty, although some critics claim that the EU's external tariff and the way in which it negotiates as one powerful body in the World Trade Organization has contributed to global poverty.

Practice questions ?

AO1 Knowledge and understanding

33 In what ways have the EU and the African Union played a role in conflict resolution? 2 marks

....

....

34 Why has the Covid-19 pandemic presented problems for the EU? 2 marks

....

....

35 Which regional organisations have taken action on climate change? 2 marks

....

....

36 In what ways do regional organisations advance human rights? 2 marks

....

....

37 To what extent are regional organisations successful in encouraging human rights?   4 marks

....

....

....

....

....

38 Why has the Arab League been so unsuccessful in providing leadership during political crises affecting the Arab world?   4 marks

....

....

....

....

....

39 Why has ASEAN been criticised over its record on human rights protection?   4 marks

....

....

....

....

....

40 How effective has NAFTA/USMCA been in encouraging economic growth and reducing poverty?   4 marks

....

....

....

....

....

Paper 3 Section A

1   Examine the main similarities and differences between the European Union
    and the Association of Southeast Asian Nations.   **12 marks**

Write a plan here, then use a separate sheet of paper to answer the question in full.

15

....

....

....

....

....

....

....

....

....

....

....

2   Examine why the European Union possesses both supranational and
    intergovernmental institutions of governance.   **12 marks**

Write a plan here, then use a separate sheet of paper to answer the question in full.

15

....

....

....

....

....

....

....

....

....

....

....

....

Paper 3 Section C

For questions 3–7, write a bullet point plan in the space provided, then use a separate sheet of paper to answer the questions in full.

3 Evaluate the extent to which the European Union is a unique example of regionalism.   **30 marks**   45

....

....

....

....

4 Evaluate the extent to which the European Union can still claim to be a successful regional body.   **30 marks**   45

....

....

....

....

5 Evaluate the extent to which the European Union is an important force in global politics.   **30 marks**   45

....

....

....

....

6 Evaluate the extent to which regional organisations are playing an increasingly important role in global politics.   **30 marks**   45

....

....

....

....

7 Evaluate the extent to which the European Union can now claim to be a supranational regional body.   **30 marks**   45

....

....

....

....